In the Net

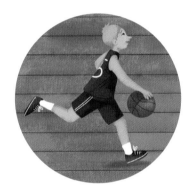

Kasia Reay

Illustrated by Malgosia Piatkowska

Schofield&Sims

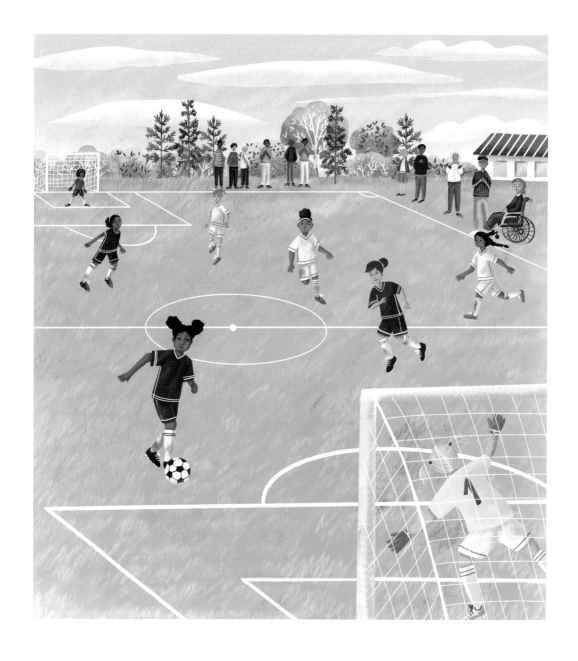

K<u>i</u><u>ck</u> it in the net.

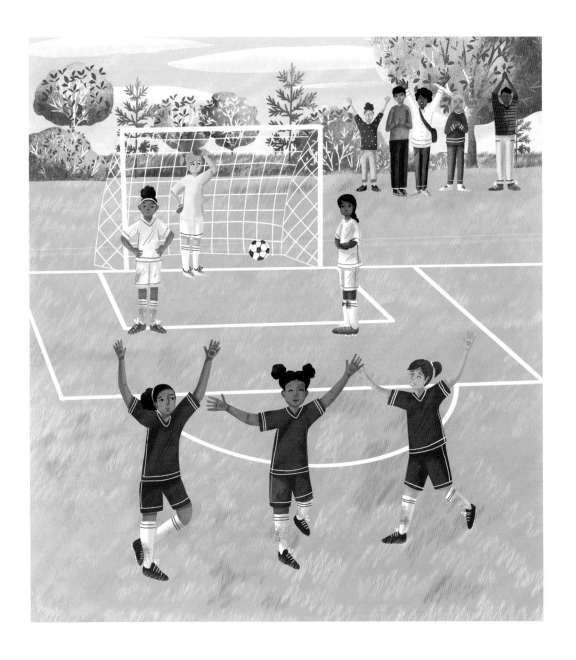

Kim got it in the net.

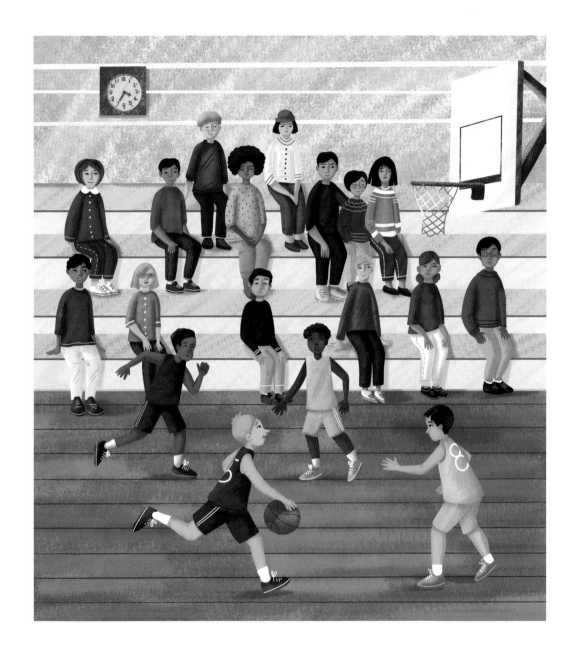

Tip it in the net.

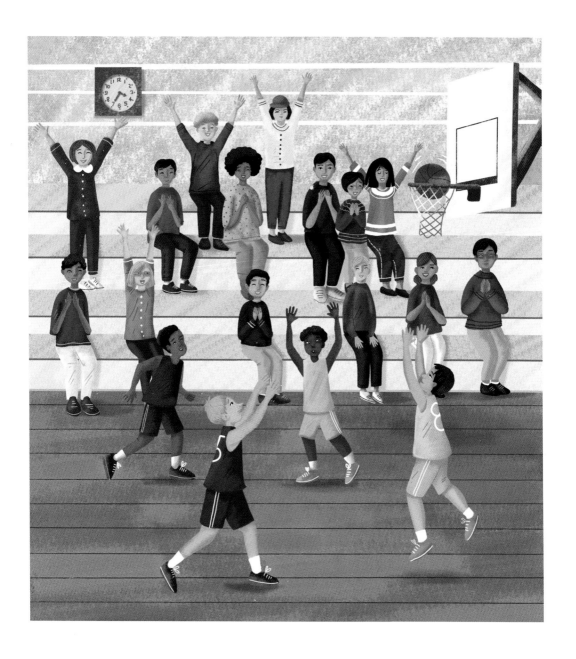

Tom got it in the net.

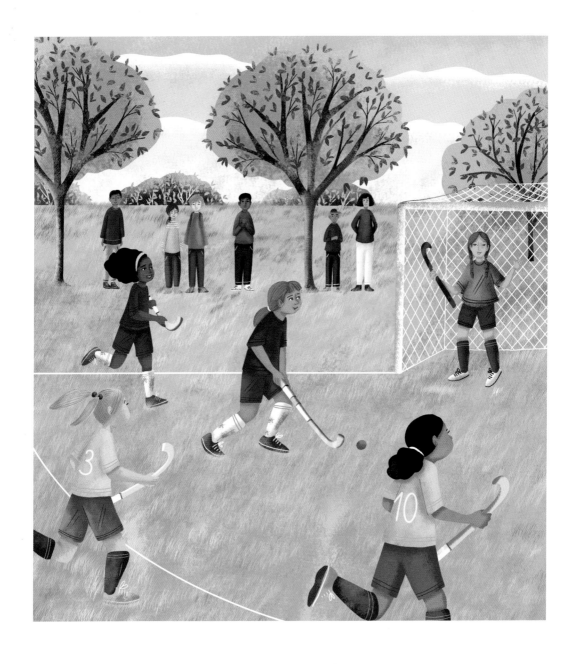

Tap it in the net.

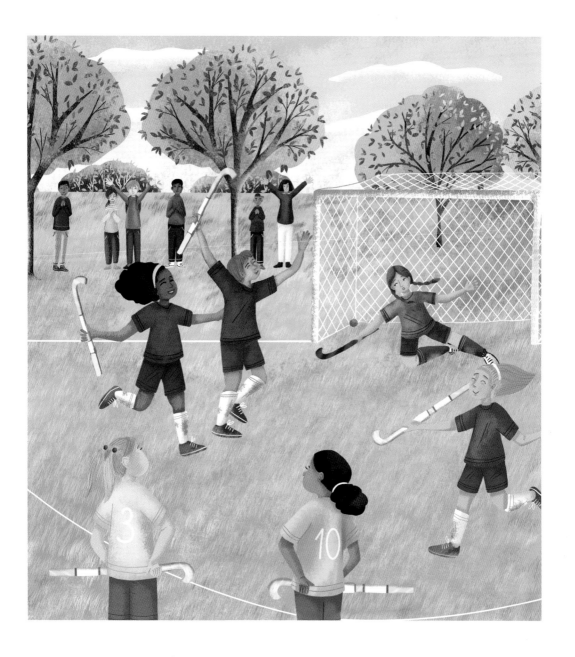

Sam got it in the net.

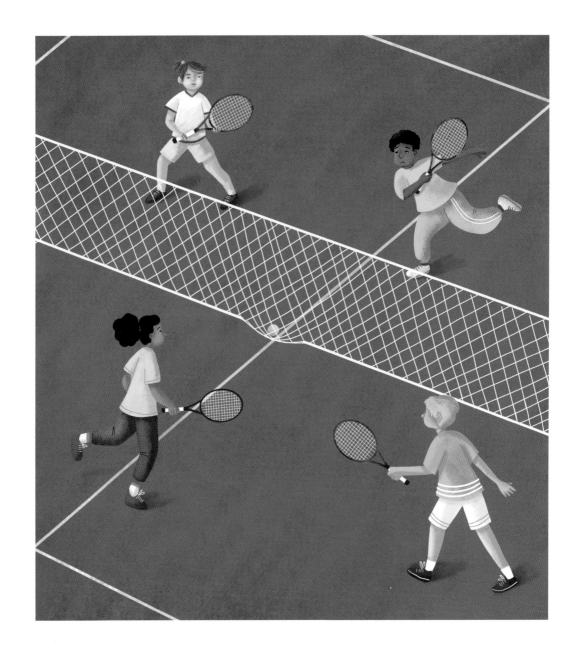

Kit got it in the net.